PENGUIN BOOKS

Published by the Penguin Group
Penguin Books Ltd, 27 Wrights Lane, London W8 5TZ, England
Penguin Books USA Inc., 375 Hudson Street, New York, New York 10014, USA
Penguin Books Australia Ltd, Ringwood, Victoria, Australia
Penguin Books Canada Ltd, 10 Alcorn Avenue, Toronto, Ontario, Canada M4V 3B2
Penguin Books (NZ) Ltd, 182–190 Wairau Road, Auckland 10, New Zealand

Penguin Books Ltd, Registered Offices: Harmondsworth, Middlesex, England

The contents of this book were first published in the USA in various issues of *Love and Rockets*
This edition first published in Penguin Books 1992
13 5 7 9 10 8 6 4

Copyright © Jaime Hernandez, 1992
All rights reserved

Printed in England by Clays Ltd, St Ives plc

JAIME HERNANDEZ

HOUSE OF RAGING WOMEN

PENGUIN BOOKS

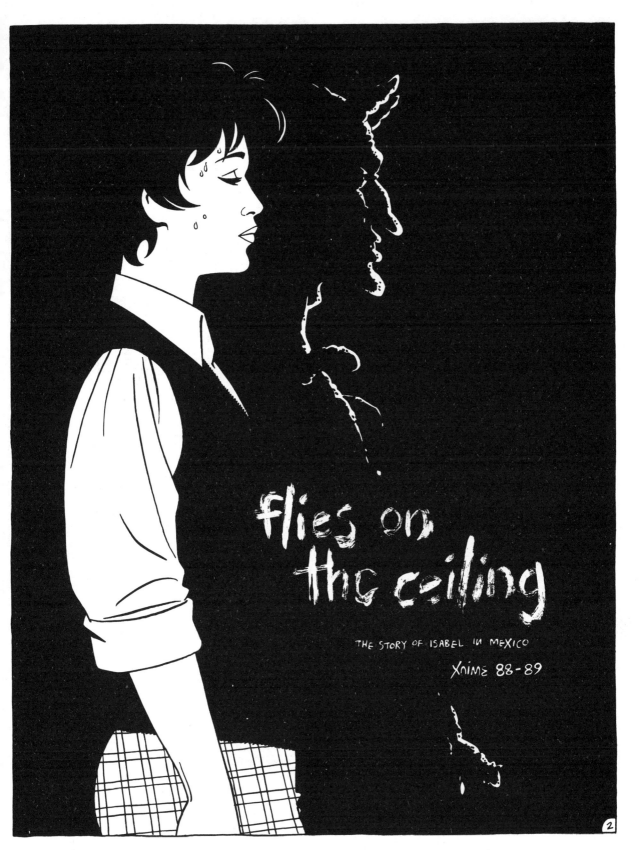

flies on
the ceiling

THE STORY OF ISABEL IN MEXICO

Xnime 88-89

HEY YOU!

NO, DON'T GO! I'M WONDERING IF YOU CAN HELP ME!

I'VE GOT A LITTLE BOY IN THERE THAT WON'T EAT. IF YOU CAN GET HIM TO, I'LL GLADLY PAY YOU.

I DON'T KNOW HOW YOU DID IT, BUT I SURE DO THANK YOU.

I USED TO HAVE TO CONVINCE MY BROTHERS TO EAT MY COOKING.

I CAN TELL YOU'RE NOT FROM AROUND HERE. DO YOU HAVE A PLACE TO STAY?

NO.

WELL, I NEED SOMEONE WHO CAN COOK AND LOOK AFTER BETO. I CAN'T PAY MUCH, BUT YOU WOULD HAVE A ROOM...

3

YOU DON'T HAVE TO EAT IN YOUR ROOM. EAT WITH US, ISABEL.

EAT WITH US!

SEE? ISN'T THIS MORE LIKE IT? NOW WE'RE MORE LIKE A FAMILY, EH?

YEAH!

4

I KNOW WHO YOU ARE.

IT'S GETTING LATE, BETO. YOUR FATHER WILL BE WORRIED.

"THAT WAS THAT. THERE WAS NOTHING LEFT FOR ME HERE. I HAD NO OTHER CHOICE BUT TO GO TO MEXICO."

WHY DID YOU MAKE ME READ THIS?

I DON'T KNOW. I THOUGHT IT WAS ONLY FAIR...

ISABEL, I'M NOT HERE TO JUDGE YOU. I COULDN'T IF I WANTED TO.

WHAT I MEAN TO SAY IS...

I WOULD LOVE YOU IF YOU WERE THE DEVIL HIMSELF.

ISABEL IS GOING TO BE MY MOTHER SOON.

6

YOU'RE NOT AFRAID ANY MORE.

ISABEL...?

HE SAID I CAN GO HOME NOW. MY FATHER IS DEAD.

HE ALSO REFUSES TO GIVE ME UP. SAYS HE'LL BE WAITING FOR ME IN THE STATES.

"I MAY TURN UP AS FLIES ON YOUR CEILING," HE SAID...

HEH. FLIES...

The End

QUEEN RENA LIFE AT 34

STILL WOMEN'S WORLD WRESTLING CHAMPION
NOW RIVAL AND FORMER TAG-TEAM PARTNER OF VICKI GLORI
STILL AVOIDING BERNIE CARBO

OH, GOD...

Y-YOU'RE CRAZY! YOU RAN RIGHT INTO ME!

I'M GONNA GET YOU ANY WAY I HAVE TO, SHARKEY.

I SWEAR, SHE STARTED IT, RENA! SHE PROVOKED ME!

REMEMBER WHAT I SAID I'D DO IF YOU LAID A HAND ON HER AGAIN?

I REMEMBER, ALL RIGHT! AND I SWORE I'D NEVER HIT HER AGAIN. BUT, SHE MADE ME, I SWEAR!

SEE LAST ISSUE "THE LITTLE MONSTER" – EL PEOR

28

SOMETIMES YOU GOTTA...

WHY DO YOU ALWAYS LISTEN TO THAT COW INSTEAD O' ME? I'M YOUR AUNT, SHRIMP! I'M FAMILY, NOT HER!

I KNOW, BUT...

YOU THINK SHE'S PRETTY HOT SHIT, HUH? ALL THOSE ADVENTURES OF HERS AND THINGS? WHY, YOU GULLIBLE LITTLE... IT'S ALL BULLSHIT, SHRIMP! THAT GIRL LIES LIKE A FIEND!

I'LL BET SHE TOLD YOU THAT THAT DAY RIGHT BEFORE OUR BIG REMATCH SHE WAS KIDNAPPED FROM THE LOCKER ROOM AND TAKEN TO ZYMBODIA WHERE THEY MADE HER THEIR QUEEN.

I THINK SHE TOLD ME SOMETHING LIKE THAT...

SEE L&R # TWO "MECHANICS" – EMIAJ

WELL, I HAPPEN TO KNOW IT'S BULLSHIT! THE GIRL GOT PREGNANT AND NEVER SHOWED UP FOR THE MATCH. AND IF YOU DON'T BELIEVE ME, THERE'S PLENTY OF PEOPLE HERE TONIGHT WHO CAN BACK UP THAT STORY. DUKE MORALES FOR ONE!

SORRY, SHRIMP. BUT IT'S TIME YOU KNEW THE TRUTH. ALL RENA TITAÑON IS AND EVER WAS IS A WRESTLER. SURE, A CHAMP AT ONE TIME, BUT THAT'S ALL. ANYONE WHO TELLS YOU DIFFERENT PROBABLY HEARD IT FROM LA TOÑA HERSELF.

OK... SEE YA.

DAMN YOU, TIA! TRYING TO TURN ME AGAINST RENA JUST BECAUSE... WELL, THAT'S COOL, 'CAUSE I DIDN'T BELIEVE YOU ANYWAY!

LOCKER

WHAT WAS WITH THE DISQUALIFICATION? EVERYBODY BEATS ON THE REFEREE NOW AND THEN, DICK!

I HAD 'EM CALL IT 'CAUSE THE SUGAR TWINS ARE TO REMAIN THE TAG TEAM CHAMPIONS! AND IF YOU EVER PULL SHIT LIKE THIS AGAIN, I'LL SEE TO IT YOU RETIRE PERMENANTLY! YOU TOO, PEPPER!

YOU'RE ALL HEART, MISTER BRAIN.

THAT'S BAIN, YOU... AND I DON'T WANT YOU EVEN GOING NEAR MY STAR'S DRESSING ROOM, Y'HEAR ME?

STAR? HE DOESN'T MEAN VICKI THE PIG LADY, DOES HE?

YEAH, SHE'S THE ONLY WRESTLER HERE THAT HAS THEIR OWN DRESSING ROOM. THE PROMOTERS REALLY ADORE HER.

SAY, LADIES! HOW ABOUT MORE QUESTIONS?

4

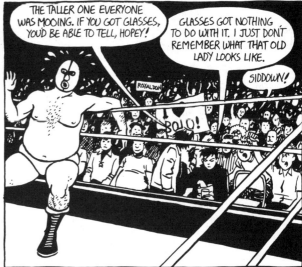

HE'S PROBABLY LIVING BEHIND SOME PUB SOMEWHERE IN ZHATO, WITH ALL THE DRINK AND WOMEN HE CAN CARRY.

HEY, I KNOW! WHY DON'T YOU AND I GO OUT DANCING TONIGHT?

SORRY, DON. I'M EXPECTING A SPECIAL GUEST TONIGHT.

DAMN IT, WOMAN! YOU DO THIS BECAUSE YOU KNOW IT DRIVES ME UP THE WALL! WHO IS THIS GUY?

YOU KNOW THIS YOUNG MAN VERY WELL, DON.

OK, OK! I'LL BE SEEING YOU! GOTTA GO!

COWARD.

HOW CAN YOU TAKE ALL THAT SHIT FROM THE AUDIENCE? I COULDN'T STAND IT MYSELF.

WE'RE USED TO IT. RENA'S HAD TO PUT UP WITH IT HER WHOLE CAREER. I'M SURE SHE'S HEARD WORSE.

...BUT, WHEN RENA WAS CHAMPION, SHE WAS LIKE, THE GOOD GUY, Y'KNOW?

IT DOESN'T MATTER. ALL FEMALE GRAPPLERS ARE TREATED SHITTY, VILLAIN OR NOT.

I MEAN, HAVEN'T YOU EVER BEEN WALKING DOWN THE STREET AND A CARLOAD OF GUYS DRIVES BY AND SHOUTS ALL KINDS OF STUPID, OBNOXIOUS SHIT?

YEAH, I GET IT. AND FOR A GIRL WHO FIGHTS IN A RING FOR A LIVING, IT'S A HUNDRED TIMES WORSE, HUH?

WELL, SURE! SO ANY TIME YOU FEEL YOU'RE HAVING IT TOUGH, THINK OF RENA, QUEEN OF THE RING. EVERYBODY'S GAL.

⑨

I'D LIKE TO STICK AROUND LONGER, RENA, BUT I GOTTA GO SEE MY KID. HE'S ALREADY LEARNING TO WORRY.

OK, BYE BYE, PEPPER. AND TELL YOUR MAMA ROSA NOT TO WORRY ANY. WE'LL GET THOSE BELTS, ALL RIGHT.

I KNEW I RECOGNIZED HER! SHE'S ROSA RICO'S KID, EH? LAST TIME I SAW HER, SHE WAS ONLY FOUR. AND NOW SHE'S YOUR TAG TEAM PARTNER! HOO HOO! WOTTA WORLD!

WHO'S ROSA RICO?

A.K.A "LA PANTERA NEGRA". SHE WAS ONE OF MY TOUGHEST RIVALS IN MY CHAMPION DAYS. YOU SEE THIS SCAR ON MY INNER THIGH?

ONE NIGHT ROSA FORGOT TO TAKE HER EARRINGS OFF FOR OUR MATCH, SO WHEN I SLAPPED THE HEAD SCISSORS ON HER...

OUCH! YOU POOR THING!

YOU MEAN POOR ROSA! HER WHOLE EAR WAS NEARLY CUT OFF.

YEOW!

YEAH, BOY! THOSE WERE SOME BATTLES!

AND JUST RECENTLY ROSA AND PEPPER HELD THE TAG TEAM BELTS TILL THOSE SUGAR TWINS CAME ALONG. I TEAMED WITH PEPPER AS A FAVOR TO ROSA TO GET THEM BACK.

BUT, WHAT ABOUT ROSA?

OH, KID. THEY BEAT ROSA SO BAD SHE WAS HOSPITALIZED FOR WEEKS. DAMN IT! WHY DIDN'T ANYONE HAVE THE HEART TO TELL HER SHE'S TOO... OLD TO... WRESTLE?

JUST BE HAPPY SHE DIDN'T END UP LIKE BULL MA...

RALPH!

WHA'D I SAY?

DON'T YOU KNOW EVERY TIME YOU OPEN YOUR MOUTH TONS OF TURDS COME OUT?

???

10

WHEN I WITNESSED YOUR DISPLAY OUT THERE TONIGHT. THE WAY YOU PARADED YOURSELF ABOUT AS THOSE PEOPLE SHOUTED THOSE FOUL NAMES AT YOU. AND YOUR GOADING AND... AND...

WELL, I MADE UP MY MIND RIGHT THEN THAT AS LONG AS YOU KEEP UP THIS... THIS... LIFESTYLE, I WILL KEEP ANTONIO AS FAR FROM YOU AS POSSIBLE.

DOES HE EVEN KNOW ABOUT THIS?

IF YOU MEAN DOES HE KNOW I WON'T LET YOU SEE HIM, YES, IT WAS DISCUSSED.

I'D PLASTER YOU ACROSS THE HALL BUT YOU'D PROBABLY TELL ANTONIO THAT... NEVER MIND.

OH, SO NOW I CAN'T EVEN BE RELATED TO VICKI GLORI WITHOUT RENA TITAÑON TURNING INTO A FULL ON BITCH! AND I CAN'T EVEN THINK ABOUT RENA TITAÑON WITHOUT VICKI GLORI--MY WONDERFUL FRIENDS...

BLEH!

I'M SO FUCKING TIRED OF THIS SHIT! OLD LADIES PLAYING JUNIOR HIGH SCHOOL GAMES. WELL, THAT'S IT, BUBBA! IT ENDS RIGHT NOW!

HEY, LITTLE GIRL! WHAT ABOUT THAT TIA OF YOURS?

DUKE, DOES RENA HAVE ANY CHILDREN?

HMM...

NO, LITTLE, GIRL. I DON'T THINK SO.

END

40

LOCAS vs LOCOS

BIG DADDY 86

SHIT, I DON'T CARE WHAT ANYONE SAYS. TO ME, MAGGIE'S STILL THE BEST... BUT WOULDN'T YOU KNOW IT, SHE STILL SEES ME AS HOPEY'S LITTLE BROTHER.

LIFE IS TOUGH, MAN.

YEAH, BUT I'LL SHOW HER. I HAVE MY LITTLE BROTHER RIGHT HERE JUST WAITING...

LITTLE IS RIGHT... HEY, ARE WE JUST GONNA WALK RIGHT IN?

WHERE'S MY RECORD, BITCH?

PIPE DOWN! CAN'T YOU SEE MAGGIE'S TRYING TO SLEEP? JESUS CHRIST!

IN THE DAY? WHAT'S SHE DOING, TAKING AFTER IZZY THE WITCH LADY?

HER BAD FOOT KEPT US UP AGAIN LAST NIGHT SO I FINALLY MADE HER DRIVE TO EMERGENCY AT FOUR IN THE MORNING. LOCO SPIDER SALAS WAS THERE. SOMEONE STUCK HIM WITH A RUSTED SCREWDRIVER BEHIND RAY'S LIQUOR.

AW, POOR BABY. SO, WHAT'S WRONG WITH HER FOOT?

ACTUALLY, IT'S HER ANKLE. SHE HURT IT WHEN SHE WAS LITTLE AND NEVER TREATED IT RIGHT. SO, ONCE IN A WHILE, IT ACTS UP ON HER... MOVE, EGGHEAD!

HEY, ARE YOU PACKING? DON'T TELL ME IZZY FINALLY GAVE YOU AN' MAGGIE HER POINTED SHOE.

YOU KIDDIN'? WE ALL GOTTA BE OUTTA HERE BY TOMORROW. I SURE WISH THEY WOULDA TOLD US SOONER. I'LL BE DAMNED IF I KNOW WHERE WE'RE LIVING NOW.

DOES THAT MEAN MY RECORD IS IN ONE OF THESE BOXES?

NO, IT'S AT DAFFY'S. HEY, DOYLE! WHEN WE FIND OUT WHERE WE'RE TAKING THIS JUNK, DO YOU THINK YOU COULD HAUL SOME OF IT IN YOUR TRUCK?

SURE, I GUESS SO.

DAFFY?! WHO GAVE YOU THE RIGHT TO LEND OUT MY RECORD?

SHE SAID SHE'D TAKE GOOD CARE OF IT.

AW, SHIT! YOU STILL HAD NO RIGHT! COME ON, DOYLE. LET'S GO TO DAFFY'S.

TALK TO YOU LATER, HOPEY.

OK.

I CAN'T BELIEVE WHAT A DREAM YOU ARE RIGHT NOW.

GUESS WHAT, IZZY. WE'VE GOT IT NARROWED DOWN TO TWO PLACES WE'RE NOT LIVING.

OH, HOPEY. I'M SURE YOUR MOTHERS WOULD LOVE TO HAVE THEIR DARLING DAUGHTERS BACK WITH THEM.

WHAT ABOUT MAGGIE'S AUNT?

NO WAY! MAGGIE'S NOT EVEN GOING NEAR THAT LADY FOR AT LEAST A YEAR! DIDN'T YOU HEAR? VICKI GLORI LOST HER CROWN LAST NIGHT.

W-WHA...? REALLY? THEN RENA TITAÑON IS CHAMPION AGAIN?

NAW, IT WAS SOME RUSSIAN LADY NAMED SULKA OR SOMETHING LIKE THAT. SHE USED THE ROPES, I THINK.

WOW, THAT'S THE KIND OF SHIT YOU JUST NEVER THINK ABOUT, Y'KNOW?

WELL, SHE AIN'T DEAD.

IT GETS YOU RIGHT BETWEEN THE EYES WHEN YOU LEAST EXPECT IT.

WHAT DOES? ISABEL, ARE YOU ALL RIGHT?

44

YOU JUST GONNA SIT THERE ALL DAY, OR WHAT?

HEY, IZZY! WHERE DO YOU WANT... WHAT'S WRONG?

I DON'T FEEL LIKE PACKING BOXES ANY MORE.

SOME PEOPLE WERE BORN OUT OF THEIR MIND. ME, I HAD TO LEARN IT THE HARD WAY!

TERRY'S LIVE-IN BOYFRIEND SAID SHE'S DOWN AT THEIR BAND'S PRACTICE PAD. LET'S HURRY BEFORE SHE LEAVES OR SOMETHING.

(SIGH) I SUPPOSE I'LL NEVER GET THAT BUCK FOR GAS, HUH?

TELEPHONE

TERRY? SHE JUST LEFT TO TALK TO HOPEY. WHAD YOU WANT HER FOR, ANYWAY?

WE BELIEVE SHE HAS JOEY'S APE SEX RECORD, ZERO.

BAM BAM

THE APE SEX ALBUM? SHE LENT IT TO ME. IF I'DA KNOWN...

AH, OUR JOURNEY ENDS...

WAIT A... YOU DIDN'T HAPPEN TO LEND IT TO... NAW... NO WAY...

WHERE THE HELL IS THAT DOYLE? I CAN'T MOVE ALL THIS SHIT WITH ALL THESE ZOMBIES LYING AROUND... ZAT HIM?

BEEP BEEP

HI, TERRY. WHATCHA DOIN' HERE?

SOMEONE TOLD ME YOU WERE BEING EVICTED. I HA TO SEE IT FOR MYSELF.

⑦

PENNY CENTURY USED TO STAY HERE WHENEVER SHE WAS IN TOWN, AND WE USED TO GET DRUNK AND EVERYTHING IN THE BACK. MRS. GALINDO DIDN'T MIND. SHE USED TO CHUG DOWN THAT NIGHT TRAIN ALL DAY LONG, PENNY WOULD TELL US.

PENNY ALSO SAID THAT THE OLD PLACE WAS SUPPOSED TO BE HAUNTED. I THINK THAT'S WHY IZZY WANTED TO MOVE HERE SO BAD. SO SHE COULD TALK WITH HER OWN KIND ONCE IN AWHILE.

THAT'S RIDICULOUS. YOU DON'T BELIEVE ALL THAT HAUNTED GARBAGE, DO YOU?

I'LL TELL YOU ONE THING: IF FLIES START GATHERING ON THE CEILING OF THIS HOUSE, I'LL BELIEVE YOU AND MAGGIE WOULD GET MARRIED.

OH, HAVE YOU TALKED TO MAGGIE ABOUT OUR DEALIE?

YES, I DID. AND TO TELL YOU THE TRUTH, I DON'T KNOW EXACTLY WHAT HER ANSWER WAS. I THINK SHE SAID YES, BUT SHE KINDA JUST BOBBLED HER HEAD AROUND, LOOKING DOWN A LOT, SHRUGGING HER SHOULDERS... YOU KNOW, THE WHOLE BIT.

HOW ABOUT IF I TALK TO HER? MAYBE I CAN CONVINCE HER THAT I'M SINCERE ABOUT THIS, AND THAT...

...YOU WANT TO JUMP MY BONES. OR IS IT MAGGIE'S BONES? OOH, TERRY! I'M JEALOUS NOW.

DAMN YOU, HOPEY! WHY DO YOU ALWAYS MAKE IT LIKE I'M THIS EVIL WITCH OUT TO RUIN EVERY... WHAT ARE YOU DOING?! STOP IT!

BUT, I THOUGHT WE WERE FRIENDS FROM NOW ON, THERESA...

C'MON, I'M SORRY, TERRY. LET'S SHAKE AND BE FRIENDS. OR WOULD YOU RATHER KISS AND MAKE UP? HUH?

GET AWAY FROM ME! I NEVER WANT TO SEE YOUR FACE OR YOUR FAT FRIEND'S FAT FACE IN MY APARTMENT EVER! I'VE HAD IT WITH YOU!

END

50

IS THE COAST CLEAR, DAFFY?

I'M NOT SURE, TOM TOM.

LET'S GO OUT THE BACK WAY IN CASE THEY'RE IN THE FRONT ROOM.

MAGGIE?! WHERE IS YOUR AUNT?

SHE STEPPED OUT AWHILE.

NO SCARS, NO BRUISES. WHAT DID SHE DO? WHAT DID SHE SAY?

BELIEVE IT OR NOT, SHE OFFERED ME A JOB.

HUH?!

SERIOUS. SHE'S STARTING A NATIONWIDE WRESTLING TOUR TOMORROW AND SHE WANTS ME TO GO ALONG. I DON'T KNOW WHAT I GOTTA DO, BUT SHE SAYS I'LL MAKE REAL GOOD MONEY.

SHE SAID, "I'M DOING THIS FOR YOU, SHRIMPO, BECAUSE I'M MOVING OUTTA STATE AFTER THIS TOUR AND I WOULDN'T WANNA LEAVE YOU OUT IN THE COLD. Y'ALL UNDERSTAND WHAT I'M SAYING?

"THIS WAY YOU CAN AFFORD TO GO LIVE WITH YOUR DYKE GIRLFRIEND BACK EAST, OR AFTER WHAT I JUST SAW IN YOUR BED, WITH YOUR BOYFRIEND. YOU HAVE UNTIL LATE AFTERNOON TO THINK ABOUT IT...

"...SO GET OFF YOUR FAT ASS AND CLEAN THIS GOD DAMNED HOUSE BEFORE I RETURN!

WELL, THAT'S THAT. I GUESS I SHOULD PACK NOW. I CAN'T AFFORD TO STAY HERE.

OOH, WHEEE! HOW COME YOU NEVER WEAR YOUR WRESTLING BOOTS ANY MORE?

SHIT, TIA WOULD SKIN ME ALIVE IF SHE KNEW I HAD THOSE. QUEEN RENA GAVE 'EM TO ME AND... WELL, I TOLD YOU ABOUT THOSE TWO...

OH, BUT THEY'RE TOO PRETTY TO SIT IN A CLOSET! IF THEY WERE MINE, I'D WEAR THEM ALL THE TIME!

I'LL GIVE 'EM TO YOU FOR YOUR LEATHER.

?

MY JACKET?! NO WAY! AS MUCH AS I LOVE THOSE BOOTS, I COULD NEVER GIVE THIS UP!

MIKE, THE SINGER OF "BLAMED YOUTH" GAVE IT TO HER!

OH, YEAH. HOW'D IT GO BETWEEN YOU AN' HIM, DAFF?

I DON'T KNOW. HE WAS WITH GOO GOO LAST NIGHT.

I TOLD YOU HE WAS A POLAR BEAR.

A WHAT?!

A POLAR BEAR. SO CUTE AND CUDDLY IN HIS CAGE BUT WHEN YOU WANT TO GET CLOSE ENOUGH TO CUDDLE HIM HE TEARS YOU APART AND SWALLOWS YOU WHOLE.

TSK! GUY! HE'S NOT LIKE THAT...

HE'S RAD!

HE'S LIKE, SO INTENSE ON STAGE! LIKE FUCKIN'...

SO INTENSE...

AND HE KNOWS JELLO...

SO RAD...

HE KNEW DARBY...

OOH...

4

I'M REALLY GLAD YOU DECIDED TO COME ALONG, SHRIMP.

I DIDN'T HAVE MUCH OF A CHOICE, DID I?

WHAT DID YOUR BOYFRIEND SAY?

HE SAYS I'M GONNA PICK HOPEY WHEN I GET BACK.

UNIGHTED ERRLIES

WELL, I'M SURE Y'ALL WILL MAKE THE RIGHT DECISION.

OH, YOU THINK SO, HUH?

Regency

REGENCY

TAKE IT EASY THE REST OF THE DAY, SHRIMP. I'LL FILL YOU IN ON WHAT YOU GOTTA DO AFTER I MAKE A FEW TV ANNOUNCEMENTS.

TAKE YOUR TIME.

LET ME GET THIS STRAIGHT, VICKI. YOU WANT TO "INSURE" YOUR WORLD CHAMPIONSHIP BELT? WELL, THAT'S QUITE AN ODD REQUEST AND I'M NOT SURE THE W.W.W. BOARD IS GOING TO GO ALONG WITH THAT.

SNORT

WHY NOT??

PAY TV PRESS 10

13

Welcome to the Regency HOTEL

Y'ALL SEEM TO FORGET THAT I COME FROM A LONG LINE OF TEXAS OIL BARONS AND I CAN MATCH ANY PRICE THEY THROW AT ME...

BUT, YOU DON'T UNDERSTAND, VICKI. I DON'T THINK YOU CAN INSURE A TITLE!

YOU'RE ALSO FORGETTING THAT I'M CHAMPION OF THE WORLD, AND IF I WANT TO BRING MY OWN PERSONAL ACCOUNTANT TO MEET WITH THE BOARD NEXT WEEK, SOMEBODY BETTER LET ME!

LET'S GO TO THE RING...

BUT, TIA. I DON'T KNOW ANYTHING ABOUT ACCOUNTING OR ANYTHING LIKE THAT!

OUCH!

YOU WON'T HAVE TO. JUST SIT THERE AN' LOOK REAL SERIOUS.

5

THE GUYS WERE ONLY KIDDING ABOUT THAT VICKI LA MOMMA JAZZ...

(PUFF PUFF) THEY SHOULDN'T JOKE LIKE THAT, CASH.

SOMEBODY'S GOTTA FEEL SORRY FOR THAT KID! I HAD TO TAKE HER IN YEARS AGO BECAUSE HER PARENTS HAD THE BALLS TO USE HER AS THEIR EXCUSE FOR BREAKING UP! JEEZ, I TOLD QUINA NOT TO MARRY MY BROTHER! HE AIN'T THE KIND THAT SHOULD EVER MARRY! BUT SHE WAS STUPID...

AN' I REALLY TRIED TO BE MORE THAN JUST AN AUNT TO THE SHRIMP IN THOSE TOUGH TIMES, BUT I DON'T THINK SHE EVER APPRECIATED IT...

EVEN NOW SHE RESENTS EVERYTHING I TRY TO DO FOR HER! HELL, NOBODY'S PERFECT! I AIN'T NO MOTHER! I'M A WRESTLER!

YEAH, BUT SHE AIN'T NO WRESTLER.

(SIGH) OK, I'LL TRY TO BE EASIER ON HER...

HUH? NOW? WHAT ABOUT OUR LITTLE AFTER HOURS DIP IN MY WATER BED, BABY?

HEY, SHRIMP! YOU UP?

IT'S OPEN.

I WAS THINKIN', SHRIMP, IF YOU WANT, TOMORROW WE COULD... WHAT THE HELL DID YOU DO TO YOUR HAIR??

I PUT SOAP IN IT. I'M DONE PLAYING YUPPIE ACCOUNTANT, Y'KNOW...

END OF PART 1

BY JAIME "THE SPINKS JINX" HERNANDEZ 88

PRINCESS WARFEATHER, CANDYCANE LAINE, BLANCHE DE LA BOOM, MRS. T., AND NOW MONTANA JANE! WHEN DOES IT ALL END, VICKI?

IT NEVER ENDS! I'M TOO FAR GONE, MEL! I'M OUTTA CONTROL!

I DON'T EVEN WANNA INSURE MY TITLE ANY MORE! I DON'T HAVE TO! AT THE RATE I'M GOING, I'LL NEVER LOSE THIS BELT! PRETTY SOON THERE'LL BE NO ONE LEFT TO CHALLENGE ME FOR IT!

MOO HOO HOO HA HA HA HAAA!

CACKLE CACKLE!

VICKI, THE BOARD SAYS IF YOU KEEP THIS UP, THEY'RE GONNA STRIP YOU OF YOUR TITLE, AND THEY AIN'T KIDDING.

I CAN'T HELP IT, CASH! EVERYTIME I SEE HER FROWNING FACE, I GO APE SHIT! SHE'S DRIVING ME NUTSO!

THEN I GUESS IT'S TIME YOU SENT HER HOME...

BULLSHIT! EVERYBODY KNOWS THAT SINCE I STARTED THIS ACCOUNTANT BIT, I'VE BEEN THE ONE SELLING OUT ALL THE ARENAS! NOT EVEN YOU HEADLINE OVER ME ANY MORE!

I GET THE FEELING THAT'S NOT THE REAL REASON YOU'RE NOT SENDING HER HOME.

NO IT AIN'T...

YOU'D THINK THAT JUST ONCE SHE'D APPRECIATE WHAT I DO FOR...

3

OH, SO MOST OF US ASK TO BE TREATED LIKE SHIT, HUH? AND EVERYBODY TALKS ABOUT WHAT A NICE GUY YOU ARE...

YOU KIDDING? NICE GUYS GET SHITTED ON.

BUT THERE ARE EXCEPTIONS TO THE RULE, RIGHT? GIVE ME A BREAK...

OF COURSE THAT'S IF YOU WANNA KEEP FOLLOWING THEM BOGUS RULES.

RAY'S GONNA HAVE TO BE REALLY SOMETHING TO FILL IN HOPEY'S SHOES LIKE HE IS...

THERE'S BEEN OTHER'S BESIDES HOPEY...

HO HO! THOSE GUYS COULDN'T EVEN LICK HOPEY'S SHOE PRINTS! SHE HAS A SPELL ON MAGGIE THAT NOT EVEN THAT CHOLO WHO WAS KILLED COULD MATCH!

I DUNNO, I THINK A LOT OF THAT HOPEY MAGIC'S FADED SINCE RAY'S COME AROUND.

MR. KNOW-IT-ALL. MAGGIE'S ONLY WITH HIM BECAUSE HOPEY DESERTED HER WHEN THE BAND WENT ON TOUR.

FUNNY, THAT'S WHAT HE SAID. AH, BUT WE'LL SEE.

YES, WE WILL SEE...

DOYLE, WHAT TIME IS IT?

FIVE MINUTES LATER THAN THE LAST TIME YOU ASKED ME. WHAT'S UP?

I PROMISED TO PICK UP MAGGIE AT THE AIRPORT AT FOUR. I'M GOING TO ASK HER BOYFRIEND IF HE'D LIKE TO GREET HER. WOULD YOU LIKE TO COME, AS WELL?

MR. KNOW-IT-ALL STRIKES AGAIN. SHALL WE GO?

9

HEY, JUST BECAUSE THE PIG LADY FIRED YOU DOESN'T MEAN YOU HAVE TO QUIT THIS BIZ ALTOGETHER! WHY DON'T YOU COME WITH US ON OUR EAST COAST TOUR?

I ADMIT, IT WON'T BE JETS, HOTELS AND LIMOS, BUT IT'LL BE A GAS ALL THE SAME! WE'RE HITTING MOST BIG CITIES, AND...

OK, MAGGIE. I KNOW HOW YOU FEEL. YOU HAVE A SAFE TRIP HOME, Y'HEAR?

THANKS, PEPPER...

NOW, BE SURE TO GET TO THE AIRPORT PLENTY EARLY SO YOU DON'T MISS YOUR PLANE. I WON'T BE AROUND TO FIX IT IF YOU SCREW UP...

TIA? COULDN'T I JUST...

NOW DON'T START AGAIN WITH THAT PHONEY BULL ABOUT HOW YOU WANT TO BE WITH ME! YOU GOT WHAT YOU WANTED, SO KNOCK IT OFF, ALREADY!

IT-IT'S NOT PHONEY BULL...

LOOK, LET'S NOT FIGHT ABOUT THIS, SHRIMP. IT'S PERFECT FOR YOU NOW. THE FINAL SALE ON MY HOUSE AIN'T FOR A FEW MONTHS, SO YOU CAN LIVE IN IT UNTIL YOU FIX YOURSELF UP, AND SINCE I'M MOVING TO TEXAS AFTER THIS TOUR, YOU WON'T EVER HAVE TO SEE ME AGAIN. AIN'T THAT GREAT?

IT'S-NOT-PHONEY-BULL.

OH, IT'S NOT, HUH? YOU THINK I NEVER KNEW ABOUT YOU AND YOUR LITTLE DYKE FRIEND LAUGHING AND CURSING ME BEHIND MY BACK? NEVER ONCE IN YOUR GOD DAMN LIFE DID YOU APPRECIATE ANYTHING I DID FOR YOU! I WAS ALWAYS SOME MONSTER TO YOU! HA! TALK ABOUT CALLING THE KETTLE BLACK!

OK...OK, THEN SO BE IT, SOVIET...

NOW WHERE THE HELL WOULD YOU BE AT SEVEN O'CLOCK IN THE MORNING?

I'LL TRY AGAIN WHEN WE REACH BLOSSOM CITY.

WHAT HAPPENED TO YOUR HAIR?

YEAH, AND IT GETS WILDER! NOT ONLY DID THE BOARD STRIP VICKI OF HER TITLE, BUT THEY ALSO BOOTED HER OUT OF THE WHOLE W.W.W. FOR GOOD.

IT AIN'T FAIR! I'VE BEEN DREAMING OF THIS REMATCH FOR WEEKS!

THEY CAN'T BOOT HER BEFORE I'VE HAD A SECOND CRACK AT HER. YOU AND I ARE GOING DOWN TO THE ARENA TO TALK TO SOMEBODY... ANYBODY!

OK, BUT AFTER SHE BROKE BIG KAT BROWN'S LEG, TOOK OUT TWO REFEREES AND BLINDED THE ANNOUNCER, WHAT WOULD YOU HAVE DONE?

THEY'VE ALWAYS HAD IT IN FOR ME, CASH. EVERYBODY KNOWS BIG KAT BROWN WEARS HER COWBOY BOOTS WAY TOO DAMN SMALL...

YEAH, THEY'RE SCUM. IT'S A GOOD THING YOU'RE OUT OF THERE...

SO, WHAT DO YOU THINK I SHOULD DO? THE JAPAN CIRCUIT? MEXICO?

I CAN'T TELL YOU WHAT TO DO, BABY, BUT AS FAR AS THIS OL' BOY'S CONCERNED, I'M GETTING OUT FOR GOOD.

16

YOU, CASH? BUT YOU STILL HAVE A GOOD THING GOING HERE.

THIRTY YEARS OF A GOOD THING IS MORE THAN ENOUGH FOR ME, BABE.

IT'S TIME I STARTED THINKING ABOUT THE REST OF MY LIFE, WHILE I STILL CAN THINK. YOU KNOW, MAYBE BUY A RANCH AND RAISE A FAMILY. I KNOW IT SOUNDS FUNNY AT MY AGE, BUT I NEVER HAD TIME FOR ANY OF THAT STUFF...

I'VE ALWAYS WANTED A FAMILY I COULD REALLY CALL MY OWN. YOU KNOW WHAT I MEAN, BABE?

YEAH... YOU'RE A NUT.

YOU EVER BEEN TO THE ZOO?

SURE. I WENT TO JUNGLELAND WHEN I WAS REAL LITTLE, BUT ALL I REMEMBER WAS DRINKING WATER FROM THE LION'S MOUTH.

I LIKE THE POLAR BEARS. I COULD SIT ALL DAY WATCHIN' 'EM.

I KNOW ALL ABOUT POLAR BEARS, BELIEVE ME...

ONE TIME I SAW ONE PLAYING WITH A KEG.

SEEMS FITTING SOMEHOW.

SHOULDN'T YOU BE AT THE ARENA RIGHT NOW?

I BROUGHT YOU HERE TO RELAX. SOMEONE LIKE YOU SHOULD RELAX MORE OFTEN.

ARE YOU RELAXING YET?

NGHHH...

17

78

82

LAS MONJAS ASESINAS

NED THE WINO 89

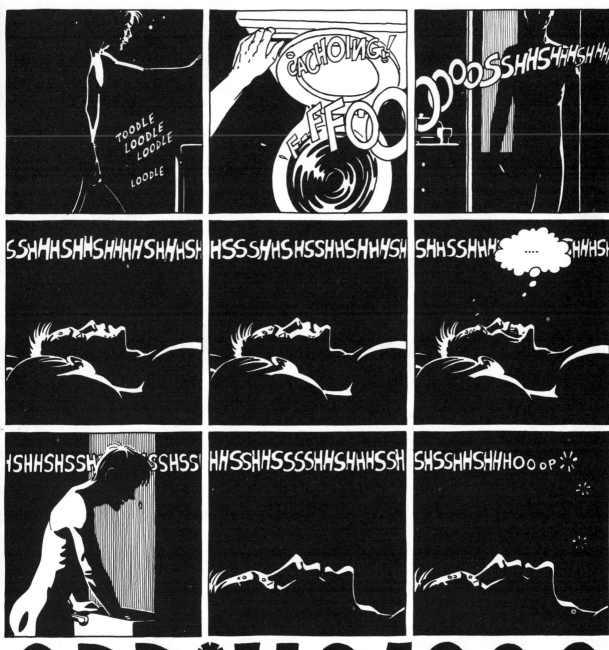

WELL, MR. DALGANG, AS USUAL YOU WERE A WONDERFUL AUDIENCE...

UH, STACY? DIDN'T WE AGREE ON THE SCHOOLGIRL UNIFORM FOR THIS TIME? I MEAN, I PAID EXTRA...

OH YEAH, WELL I FIGURED IT WOULD BE KIND OF AWKWARD SINCE LILY DIDN'T HAVE ONE AND... MAYBE NEXT TIME, DALGANG?

BUT, I PAID... WELL, ALL RIGHT. NEXT TIME.

DON'T SPEND IT ALL AT ONCE, EH, PRETTY BOY?

I STILL DON'T SEE WHAT'S SO HARD ABOUT JUST SITTING THERE AND THEN COLLECTING MONEY. PLEASE, HONEY. TALK TO ME. DOYLE...?

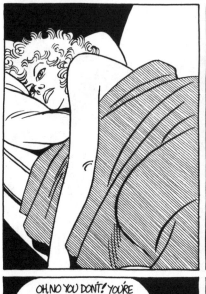

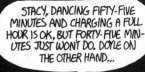

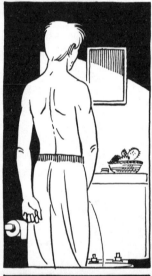

BELOW MY WINDOW LURKS MY HEAD

BY
XAIME
1989

WHAT'S THAT? OK, I'LL TALK TO YOU SOON. BYE, MAGGIE...

GLOOM

HEY! HEY!

HEY, RAY! YOU STILL LIVE UP THERE?

YEAH, COME ON UP, DOYLE, YOU BUM!

OIN WASH

LOOKS A HELL OF A LOT BETTER THAN WHEN I LIVED HERE.

IT'S BEEN AWHILE, MAN. WHERE YOU BEEN HIDING YOURSELF?

I'VE BEEN SLEEPING AT THE MISSION LATELY. IT'S BEEN COLD, Y'KNOW...

YOU WANNA STAY HERE? MAGGIE'S STILL AWAY...

NAW, S'COOL. BUT I COULD USE A SHOWER...

SURE, SURE! HELP YOURSELF! ANYTHING YOU WANT!

WHAT'S WITH THE HOSPITALITY, MAX?

I'M HAPPY TO SEE YOU! YOU'RE LOOKING AT ONE LONELY SON OF A BITCH!

2

SO THEN... DOES THIS MAKE IT OFFICIAL?

C'MON, ELIAS...

I KNEW IT WAS PRETTY MUCH OVER BETWEEN MAGGIE AND ME WHEN SHE AND HOPEY WERE REUNITED. BUT I KEPT MOPING AND HOPING ANYWAY...

THEN ONE DAY I RAN INTO DANITA AND SHE WAS REALLY SAD TO HEAR ABOUT MAGGIE AND ME...

"SHE THEN ASKED ME IF I STILL PAINTED, AND TO CHEER ME UP, OFFERED TO POSE FOR ME. IT WAS NEVER ANY SECRET TO HER HOW MUCH I'VE AL- WAYS ADMIRED HER RATHER ROBUST PHYSIQUE. AND HEY, SHE WOULDN'T HAVE TO WORRY ABOUT ME, ALL I HAD ON MY MIND WAS MAGGIE...

SOMETIMES ANYWAY...

"DANITA BECAME A REAL COMFORTING FRIEND AS THE DAYS PASSED. IT WASN'T UNTIL SHE OFFERED TO POSE NUDE THAT I REALIZED SHE WAS INTERESTED IN BEING SOMETHING MORE THAN A COMFORTING FRIEND...

AFTER THAT, THINGS PRETTY MUCH FELL INTO PLACE. EVERYTHING'S COOL NOW. I MEAN, MAGGIE'S HAPPIER NOW WITH HOPEY, ISN'T SHE? I'M HAPPY WITH DANITA NOW...

SO WHAT'S THE FUCKING PROBLEM?

4

I KEEP HAVING THIS REOCCURRING NIGHTMARE WHERE MAGGIE DOESN'T KNOW SHE AND I HAVE SPLIT UP...

I DON'T THINK ME AN' ELIAS SHOULD STAY HERE ANY MORE.

WHY NOT?

WELL, WHAT IF ELIAS'S DADDY FINDS US HERE AN' GOES OFF AN' SHOOTS YOU, OR SOMETHIN'! HE'S BEEN KNOWN TO DO SHIT LIKE THAT!

HE'S NOT GOING TO FIND YOU. HE DOESN'T KNOW ME...

WELL, WE CAN'T STAY HERE JUST THE SAME. IT DON'T FEEL RIGHT...

MMM...

WOULD YOU FEEL BETTER IF I TOLD YOU WE'RE NOT DOING ANYTHING WRONG?

PROBABLY NOT...

MMM... ZZZZZZZ

END OF PART ONE

BELOW MY WINDOW LURKS MY HEA PART 2

...THEN CORNELIUS STABBED THE GUY IN THE THROAT. THATS WHY HE LEFT STOCKTON AN' CAME HERE. I MET HIM AT A PARTY...

ONE TIME HE GOT SO MAD HE WAS GONNA STAB ME. SO RIGHT THEN I TOLD 'IM I WAS PREGNANT. SO HE JUST UP AN' LEFT TOWN...

AN' EVERY ONCE IN AWHILE, HE COMES BACK TO SEE ELIAS. BUT HE'S GETTIN' SCARIER EVERY VISIT. HE BEAT UP MY DADDY LAST TIME...

NOK NOK N

MAMA, THE DO'...

I'LL GET IT.

DANITA, WAIT...

K NOK NOK NOK NOK

IT'S ABOUT TIME I FOUND YOU!

SO, YOU FOUND ME. SO WHAT?

HOWARD 99

I JUST CAME TO WARN YOU THAT CORNELIUS IS LOOKING FOR YOU...

RAY, DO YOU KNOW RONNIE?

CLIPPERS

MAD? NAW, I'LL BET BY NOW SHE'S EVEN FORGOTTEN HIS NAME. HATE TO SAY IT, GUY, BUT YOU'RE JUST NO HOPEY.

ANYWAY, I HOPE YOU TWO HAVE A WONDERFUL, LASTING RELATIONSHIP EVEN THOUGH WHAT'S-HIS-NAME WITH THE KNIFE WILL DO EVERYTHING IN HIS POWER TO TRY AND STOP IT.

JUST KIDDING...

WELL, IT'S LATE, SO WE BETTER GET GOING. ELIAS, LET'S GO. GET YOUR JACKET...

? AHEM ?

WE GOIN' HOME NOW?

BABY, I NEVER WANTED TO GET YOU INVOLVED IN THIS. YOU DON'T WANT ANY PART OF MY TROUBLES.

WHY DON'T YOU LET ME DECIDE ON WHAT I WANT AND DON'T WANT.

HEY, DON'T GET MAD. IT'S NOT LIKE I'M GONNA FORGET YOU OR ANYTHING. I'LL BE AROUND. I PROMISE.

C'MON, ELIAS.

CAN WE GO TO CARLOS'S HOUSE TO-MORROW? HE SAID HIS DADDY GOTS JUST ONE EYE...

OFTEN OF-TEN OFFEN...

2+2=5

4

113

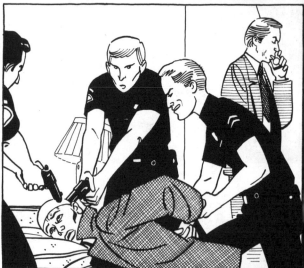

THE END

BOXER,
BIKINI,
BRIEF

1776

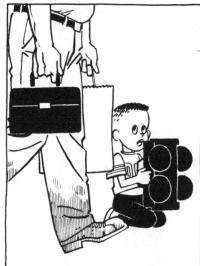

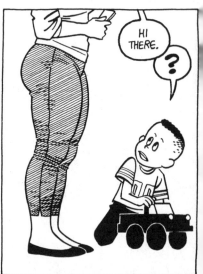

NINETY-THREE MILLION MILES FROM THE SUN

...AND COUNTING

BY the FAKE Santa CLAUS 88

②

126

(SIGH) OK... IT WAS REALLY NICE HAVING YOU HERE JUST THE SAME. I'LL TELL HOPEY YOU SAID HI...

Y-YOU'VE TALKED TO HER LATELY?

UH... WELL, YEAH. ABOUT TWO WEEKS AGO...

I WAS JUST WALKING DOWN THE STREET AND SHE JUST KINDA SAID HI...

I CAN'T LIE TO YOU, MAGGIE! I DID SEE HER TWO WEEKS AGO... BUT IN THE HOSPITAL!

H-HOSPITAL? WHAT HAPPENED TO HER?

MAGGIE, OPEN YOUR EYES! DO I LOOK LIKE I JUST HAD A BABY TWO WEEKS AGO?!?

THEN... THEN... THEN...

I PROMISED HER I WOULDN'T TELL A SOUL. BUT I JUST COULDN'T KEEP IT FROM YOU! HOPEY WAS SO FREAKED OUT BY HER PREGNANCY THAT I TOLD HER I'D TAKE THE BABY AND PRETEND SHE WERE MY OWN AS LONG AS SHE WENT THROUGH WITH THE BIRTH...

PENNY, WHERE IS SHE? PLEASE, I GOTS TO KNOW...

PLEASE, RAY? JUST ONE MORE DAY, AND THEN I PROMISE WE'LL LEAVE.

... OK.

♪ ...TODOS LOS NEGROS TOMAMOS CAFÉ... ♪

133

HEY MA--

♪

:SNIFF:

YOU OK?

HUH? OH, YEAH... RAY HAS TO GET BACK HOME TO WORK.

YOU'RE NOT GOING WITH HIM?

NOT YET. THERE'S SOMETHING I GOTS TO KNOW FIRST...

PENNY

?

PLEASE SHOW THEM IN, DEMOÑA.

YOU TOLD MAGGIE THAT YOUR KID WAS MY KID!

SURE I DID. HOW ELSE WAS I GONNA GET YOU TWO TOGETHER AGAIN?

BY THE WAY, YOUR SEAMS ARE CROOKED, PENNY!

OH. YOU KNOW ABOUT THAT...

NO DUH, HUH?

JUST GO TO HELL, PENNY! C'MON, MAG! WE'RE OUTTA HERE...

18

"WE RAN INTO SOME HIPPIES WHO PROMISED US A PLACE TO STAY IF WE JOINED THEIR BAND. WE WERE BOOTED AFTER OUR FIRST GIG (FOLLOWING TWO PRACTICES) BECAUSE...WELL, I STILL CAN'T STAND GODDAMN HIPPIES! NEVER COULD, NEVER WILL..."

"I COULD TELL TEX WAS GETTING REAL TIRED OF PLAYING 'MUSICAL HOUSES,' SO ONE NIGHT, TOTALLY RAGGED OUT, I GIVE HIM THE WORKS. I CALL HIM SPINELESS AND DARE HIM TO GO HOME TO HIS FOLKS. HELL, I NEVER THOUGHT HE'D TAKE ME UP ON IT! HE LEFT ME STANDING IN THE RAIN AT FOUR IN THE MORNING AND DIDN'T LOOK BACK ONCE. WHY DOES THE WORD 'WIMP' DO THAT TO GUYS, ANYWAY?"

"SO NOW I'M ALONE, AND I DECIDE TO TRY GETTING HOME. WELL, OL' PENNY'S ON VACATION SOMEWHERE, AND MOM... WELL, RIGHT THEN IT WAS TIME FOR SERIOUS TACTICS. THOSE OTHER LADIES WEREN'T TOO HAPPY ABOUT ME HOGGING THEIR TURF. JEEZ, I ONLY NEEDED ONE CUSTOMER..."

"ANYWAY, ME AN' THIS OLD FUCKER WENT DOWN TO THIS OLD HOTEL THAT HIS BROTHER IN LAW OWNED IN THE FIFTIES OR SOME SHIT LIKE THAT. MAN, I HAD HIS WALLET AND WAS OUTTA THERE BEFORE HE COULD UNTIE HIS FIRST SHOE..."

"HE HAD JUST ENOUGH CASH TO GET ME TO I-DIDN'T-CARE-WHERE, JUST FAR ENOUGH AWAY FROM THAT SICK OLD CITY..."

"IN LINE TO GET MY TRAIN TICKET I DID SOMETHING I HADN'T DONE SINCE KINDERGARTEN. I PASSED OUT. GUESS I SHOULDA USED SOME OF THAT CASH FOR FOOD, HUH?"

"ALL I REMEMBER IS THAT STUPID LADY'S VOICE SAYING 'JUST STEP OVER HER! WE'RE IN A HURRY!' OVER AND OVER AND OVER..."

"I WAKE UP IN SOME MEDICAL CLINIC WITH A HEADACHE THE SIZE OF ASIA, ALL MY MONEY'S GONE AND TO MAKE MATTERS WORSE, THE DOCTOR TELLS ME THE MAIN REASON I PASSED OUT. HE SAYS I'M PREGNANT. I SAY HE'S NUTS. HE SAYS I'M OVER THREE MONTHS. I BAWL.

"NEXT I ASK THE QUACK FOR THE NEAREST ABORTION CLINIC, BUT HE TELLS ME I'M TOO FAR INTO MY PREGNANCY. THAT IT WOULD BE WAY TOO DANGEROUS FOR ME. WELL, BY THIS TIME I'M REALLY SCREWED UP, SO I HEAD STRAIGHT FOR THE NEAREST RIVER TO JUMP INTO WHEN ALL OF A SUDDEN I SPOT A FAMILIAR, ROUND SHAPE ON THE OTHER SIDE...

"ME AN' TEX ARE ONCE AGAIN TRAVELLING PARTNERS AND WHEN I TELL HIM OF MY SITUATION, HE ODDLY REPLIES...

HUH, THAT'S FUNNY. SO IS PENNY...

"AND WOULDN'T YOU KNOW WHEN WE GET TO PENNY'S, SHE'S ALL HAPPY AND BUBBLY AND SHE'S STUFFED HALF HER HOUSE WITH BABY STUFF. JUST WHAT I NEEDED TO SEE...

"ONCE WE COMPARE STORIES AND STOMACHS, IT DOESN'T TAKE ME LONG TO FIGURE OUT SOMETHING PENNY AND TEXAS ALREADY KNOW. THAT WE BOTH GOT POKED ON THE SAME NIGHT, BY THE SAME GUY! DO I HAVE TO SPELL OUT HIS NAME?

HEH!

"IT'S REALLY STUPID, BUT WHEN ME AN' TEX WERE LIVING HERE IN THE MANSION ABOUT A YEAR AGO, ME AN' PENNY USED TO TEASE THE POOR BOY WITH THE GARTERS. YOU KNOW, LIKE ME AN' YOU DID WITH SPOOKY THE SMOKEY...?

"WELL, HEH, ONE NIGHT WE WERE ALL GETTING REALLY FUCKED UP ON EVERYTHING AND ANYTHING AND.... WELL, I DON'T REMEMBER MUCH OF THAT NIGHT, BUT PENNY DOES. SHE EVEN TOLD HER HUSBAND ABOUT IT. I GUESS HE WAS JUST HAPPY THAT SOMEBODY WOULD GET HIM A SON, SINCE HE COULDN'T HIMSELF. OLD GOAT...

21

"ANYWAY, ON THE DAY I WENT INTO LABOR, THAT WHOLE TIME I KEPT WONDERING WHAT I WOULD HAVE DONE THAT DAY AT THE RIVER IF OL' TEX WASN'T THERE. MAN, I STILL WONDER ABOUT THAT, BUT NOT AS MUCH AS I DID THAT DAY..."

"BY THE WAY, I WASN'T TOO SURPRISED WHEN I MISCARRIED, BUT PENNY TOOK IT LIKE THERE WAS NO LONGER SUCH A THING AS ICE CREAM. SHE EVEN TRIED TO GIVE ME HER BABY THAT SHE HAD TWO DAYS EARLIER, WITH GREAT SUCCESS, I MIGHT ADD. AND THAT WAS TWO MONTHS AGO, NOT TWO WEEKS. I SWEAR..."

ANYWAY, SINCE THEN TEX AND I HAD BEEN LIVING WITH SOME PEOPLE WHO TURNED OUT TO BE MAJOR CRACK MAFIA. THAT'S WHY YOU FOUND ME IN JAIL...

... AND... THAT'S ALL...

I-I'M SORRY...

WHAT ARE YOU SORRY ABOUT? THE KID'S BETTER OFF! CAN YOU IMAGINE ME BEING ITS MOM?! C'MON, MAG...

♫ STODOLA STODOLA STODOLA PUMPA— STODOLA PUMPA— STODOLA PUM

YOO HOO! IS EVERYTHING ALL HUNKYDORY?

YES, PENELOPE. EVERYTHING IS ALL HUNKYDORY.